1 Market Size and Market S

Question 1

Which of the following businesses has the lowest market share?

Business	Market Size by Value	Total Sales
A	£240m	£20m
B	£150m	£18m
C	£80m	£10m

Question 2

A market has a market size by value of £4bn. The chart opposite shows the market share of the 5 businesses operating within this market. Using the information provided, calculate the sales revenue of each business in this market.

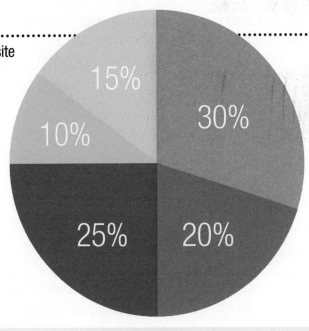

- Business A
- Business B
- Business C
- Business D
- Business E

Question 3

A gym currently has 100 members. Yearly membership is £480. The gym expects the local market for gym memberships to increase, resulting in a 10% increase in memberships per year, for the next 3 years. The membership fee is predicted to remain the same during this time. Calculate the difference in sales revenue between now and in three years time.

Question 4

This year, the market size of widgets by volume is estimated to be 472,500. This would represent a 5% increase from last year. Calculate the number of widgets sold last year.

Question 5

Last year, a UK manufacturer of condiments achieved its highest sales revenue of £575.000. This represented a 7% share of the total market. Using the information provided, calculate the market size by value of condiments in the UK.

EDEXCEL A-LEVEL BUSINESS

CALCULATION PRACTICE BOOK

Student Name:

Contents

Remember, always show your workings

Written by: Graham Prior

Question 6

The total market value of a market in 2016 was £5bn. The market has grown, on average, by 6% per year since 2012. If this level of growth continues, calculate the market size by value in 2018.

Question 7

This year, a business estimates that its sales revenue will be £69,525, an increase of 3% from the year before. The market size by value of the market the business operates in is forecast to be £459,000 this year, which is 2% higher than last year. Calculate the market share of the business last year.

Question 8

An Italian restaurant in Weardale is considering offering a takeaway pizza service. The restaurant estimates that it will sell 2,500 pizzas a year, charging £5 per pizza. This would give the restaurant a 10% share of the local market. Calculate the size of the market by volume and value for takeaway pizzas in Weardale.

Question 9

Business A sold 150,000 units in the UK last year. It estimates that this will increase by 35% this year and that its market share will be 25%. Calculate the total size of the market by volume.

Question 10

In 2014, the size of a market by value was £4m. In 2015, it was £4.6m and in 2016 it was £5.29m. A business operating in this market estimates that in 2017, its sales revenue will be £1.52m. Calculate the market share of the business in 2017, assuming the same level of market growth that occurred between 2014 and 2016 continues in 2017.

2 Price and Income Elasticity of Demand

Price Elasticity of Demand

Question 1
A business sells 500 products per week and estimates that the price elasticity of demand for its products is -0.4. The business is considering increasing the price by 10%. Calculate the quantity that will be demanded after the price increase.

Question 2
A burger van estimates that the price elasticity of demand of its burgers is -2. The owner of the burger van is considering reducing the price of the burgers from £2 to £1.60. The burger van sells an average of 800 burgers per week. Calculate the quantity that will be demanded at the new price.

Question 3

After a business increased the price of its products from £10 to £15, weekly demand fell from 5,000 units per week to 4,000 units per week. Calculate the price elasticity of demand.

Question 4

An ice cream van charges £1 for an ice cream and sells, on average, 600 ice creams per week. The owner is considering reducing the price by 20%. The owner estimates that the price elasticity of demand is -3. Calculate the percentage weekly increase in revenue if the owner increases the price.

Question 5

Below is a table of data relating to a business. The business estimates that the price elasticity of demand of its products is -0.2 and is considering increasing the price from £50 to £60. Based on this information and the information in the table below, calculate how much extra (weekly) profit the business would make if it increased the price.

Weekly Sales	400 units
Variable Cost Per Unit	£10
Weekly Fixed Costs	£10,000

Income Elasticity of Demand

Question 1

A small coffee shop sells 800 cups of coffee per month and the owner believes that the income elasticity of demand for coffee is +0.8. Demand for coffee has risen to 832 cups per month. Calculate the percentage increase in income in the local area.

Question 2

A luxury TV manufacturer saw sales increase from 5,000 units per year to 6,400 units each year, due to a 7% increase in income levels. Calculate the income elasticity of demand.

Question 3

A supermarket selling budget brands estimates that the income elasticity of demand for its products is -0.3. The supermarket sells all products for 99p and sold 25,000,000 units nationwide in 2016. The supermarket estimates that in 2017, incomes will increase nationally by 2.3%. Based on this information, calculate the expected revenue for 2017.

Question 4

Below is chart showing the index for the income of a town in North East England. It is believed that the income elasticity of demand for luxury handbags is +1.3. The base year is 2015, when 1,800 handbags were sold in the town. Using this information, and the information in the chart, calculate the number of luxury handbags sold in the town in 2016.

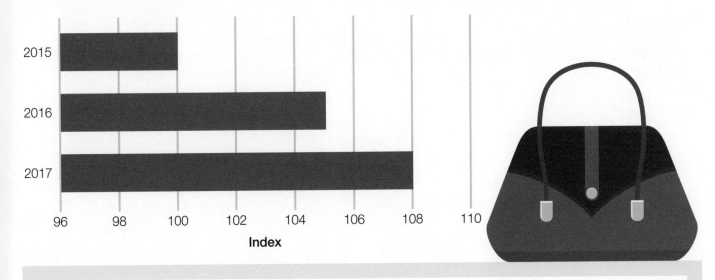

Question 5

A bakery, which opens Monday to Saturday, sells bread rolls for 24p and ciabattas for £1.35. The bakery estimates that the income elasticity of demand for bread rolls is +0.4 whereas the income elasticity of demand for ciabattas is +2. The local area is suffering from the closure of a large employer, resulting in a fall in the average income of 5%. The bakery currently sells 400 bread rolls and 100 ciabattas per day. Based on the fall in income, calculate the new daily demand for bread rolls and ciabattas and the difference in weekly revenue.

3 Cost Plus Pricing

Question 1

A table manufacturer adds a 20% mark-up to the unit cost of each table. The unit cost per table is £50. Calculate the selling price per table.

Question 2

A bakery sells its pasties for £1.20 per pasty. The unit cost per pasty is £0.75. Calculate the percentage mark-up.

Question 3

A business sells its products for £4 per unit. The unit cost per product is 4/5 of the selling price. Calculate the percentage mark-up.

Question 4

Below is a table showing the unit cost of two products made by a manufacturer.

Product	Unit Cost
A	£2.20
B	£2.50

The manufacturer adds a 20% mark-up on each product. Last month, the manufacturer sold 5,000 units of product A and 3,000 units of product B. Calculate the total sales revenue from product A and product B last month.

Question 5

Last month, a plastic box manufacturer sold 8,000 plastic boxes, achieving a total revenue of £40,000. The manufacturer adds a 25% mark-up to the unit cost of each plastic box. Calculate the unit cost per plastic box.

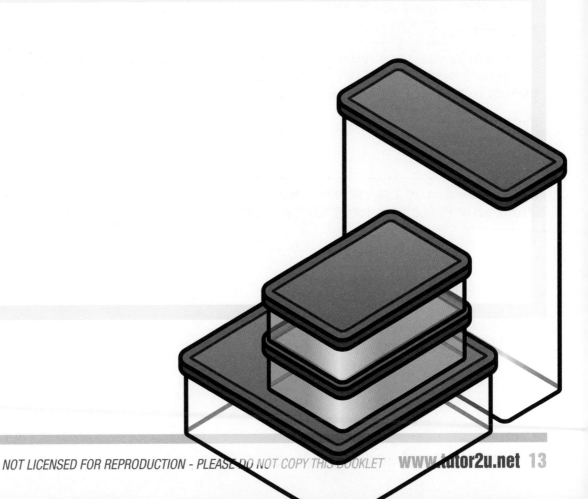

4 Cash Flow Forecasts

Question 1

A business estimates that in October, its total inflows will be £10,000 and its total outflows will be £4,000. The closing balance in September was £8,000. Calculate the closing balance for October.

Question 2

Below is a cash flow forecast for a small business. Complete the cash flow forecast by calculating the missing figures.

	January	February	March
Cash Inflows	£10,000		£13,000
Cash Outflows		£5,000	£5,500
Net Cash Flow	£6,000	£7,000	
Opening Balance	£3,000		£16,000
Closing Balance		£16,000	

Question 3

The business in question 2 now believes that in March, cash inflows will be £15,000 instead of £13,000 and cash outflows will be £7,000 instead of £5,500. Calculate the new closing balance for March.

Question 4

A newsagent estimates that between January and March, total inflows will be £15,000. 25% of the inflows will be in January, 30% in February and the remainder in March. Total outflows between January and March are estimated to be £7,000, of which 15% will be in January, 25% in February and 60% in March. The opening balance in January is £2,500. Using this information, complete the cash flow forecast below.

	January	February	March
Cash Inflows			
Cash Outflows			
Net Cash Flow			
Opening Balance			
Closing Balance			

Question 5

A small restaurant has produced the cash flow forecast shown below.

	Quarter 1	Quarter 2
Cash Inflows	£25,000	£33,000
Cash Outflows	£60,000	£21,000
Net Cash Flow	(£35,000)	£12,000
Opening Balance	£24,000	(£11,000)
Closing Balance	(£11,000)	£1,000

The owner now believes that some of the information is incorrect. The owner estimates that in quarter 1, inflows will be 25% higher and outflows will be 10% higher whereas in quarter 2, inflows will be 30% higher and outflows will be 15% higher. The opening balance remains the same. Amend the cash flow forecast based on the information given using the blank cash flow forecast below.

	Quarter 1	Quarter 2
Cash Inflows		
Cash Outflows		
Net Cash Flow		
Opening Balance		
Closing Balance		

Question 6

Opposite is a cash flow forecast for a coffee shop. The owner estimates that in quarter 2, cash inflows will be 3/5 higher than quarter 1, whereas cash outflows will increase by 3/4. Using this information, calculate the closing balance for quarter 2.

	Quarter 1	Quarter 2
Cash Inflows	£7,000	
Cash Outflows	£3,200	
Net Cash Flow	£3,800	
Opening Balance	£2,000	
Closing Balance	£5,800	

Question 7

The owners of a business are drawing up a cash flow forecast for January, February and March. They estimate that in January, revenue will be £20,000. This is expected to rise by 25% each month up to and including March. This is due to the owners spending £4,000 on marketing in January. Other costs are as follows:

- £6,250 per month on wages
- £1,050 loan repayments in February and March
- Additional costs per month equal to 15% of monthly revenue

The opening balance is £15,000. Using the information, complete the cash flow forecast below.

	January	February	March
Inflows			
Revenue			
Total Inflows			
Outflows			
Marketing			
Wages			
Loan Repayments			
Additional Costs			
Total Outflows			
Net Cash Flow			
Opening Balance			
Closing Balance			

Question 8

A small manufacturing business has a closing balance of £250,000. Net cash flow is 2/5 of the closing balance and total outflows are 1/4 of the net cash flow. Calculate the total cash inflow figure for the manufacturing business using the information given.

Question 9

Below is a chart showing the forecasted inflows and outflows for a flower shop. Using the information in the chart, complete the cash flow forecast. The opening balance in month 1 is £0.

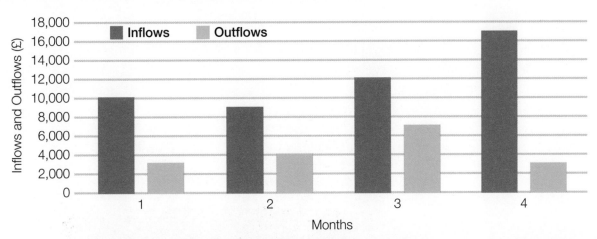

	Month 1	Month 2	Month 3	Month 4
Cash Inflows				
Cash Outflows				
Net Cash Flow				
Opening Balance				
Closing Balance				

Question 10

Next month, a garage that specialises in servicing commercial vehicles, is considering offering 50% of its customers a two month credit period for payment, as opposed to asking all its customers to pay up front. The owner of the garage has also managed to increase the time it needs to make its payments by negotiating with some of its suppliers. As of next month, 60% of the garages outflows will be payable immediately with the rest payable in one month's time. Outflows are estimated to be 2/5 of revenue each month.

The owner of the garage estimates that revenue next month will be £40,000. Calculate the total cash inflows, total cash outflows and net cash flow for next month.

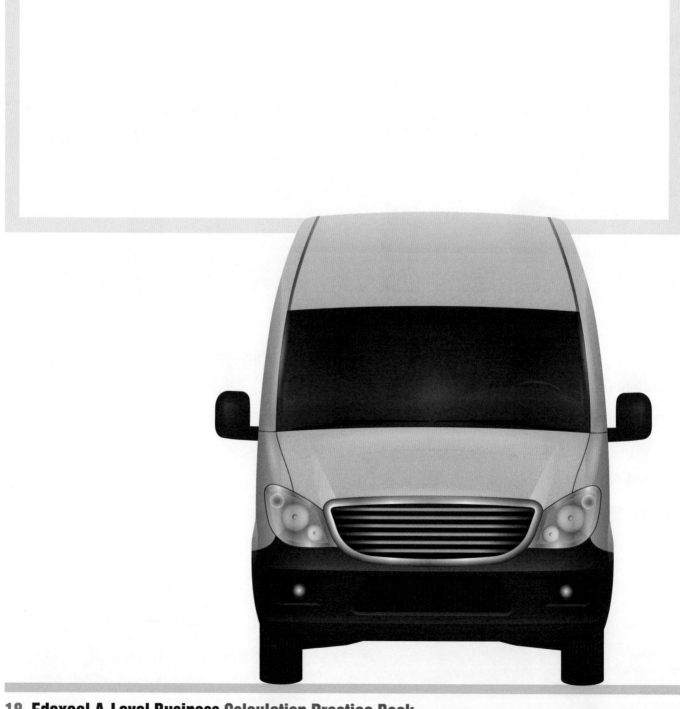

5 Sales, Revenue and Costs

Question 1

Last year, a business sold 250,000 products priced at £2.50 per product. Calculate the sales revenue of the business last year.

Question 2

A mobile coffee van charges £1.80 for a cup of coffee. Last month, the sales revenue of the coffee van was £9,000 and the total variable costs were £4,000. Calculate how many cups of coffee the van sold last month and the variable cost per cup.

Question 3

Last year, a business sold 500,000 units priced at £3.50 per unit. Variable cost per unit is £1.50. This year, the business has increased the selling price by 1/5 and the business estimates that this will result in the number of units sold falling by 12%. Calculate the estimated sales volume, sales revenue and total variable costs for this year.

Question 4

Below is a table of data relating to a business last year.

Number of units sold	150,000
Unit cost	£2.50
Percentage mark-up	10%

The business estimates that this year, it will sell 15% more units than last year and that due to an increase in supplier costs, the cost per unit will increase by 8%. Calculate the estimated sales volume and sales revenue for this year, assuming the percentage mark-up remains the same as last year.

Question 5

A television manufacturer sells its televisions to retailers for £120 a set. Variable costs are 2/5 of the selling price, with monthly fixed costs being £75,000. The manufacturer sells 1,400 televisions per month. Calculate the yearly profit of the business.

Question 6

A business estimates that it will make a profit of £250,000 this year. The business estimates that it will sell 150,000 units, with a selling price of £10 per unit. Variable costs per unit are 25% of the selling price. Calculate the estimated fixed costs of the business.

Question 7

Last month, a florist sold 910 bunches of flowers making a profit of £2,005. Fixed costs are £3,000 per month and the selling price of a bunch of flowers is £7.50. Calculate the variable cost of a bunch of flowers.

Question 8

Next year, a business estimates that it will sell 25,000 units at a selling price of £12 per unit. Variable costs per unit are 1/3 of the selling price and the business estimates that the business will make a profit of £80,000. Calculate the fixed costs of the business for next year.

Question 9

Below is a chart showing the number of units a business sold this year and last year. The variable cost per unit has remained at £1.50 during these two years and the selling price has remained at £2.85. Fixed costs last year were £15,000 but this year, due to expansion and moving to larger premises, they increased by 15%. Calculate the percentage increase in profit between this year and last year.

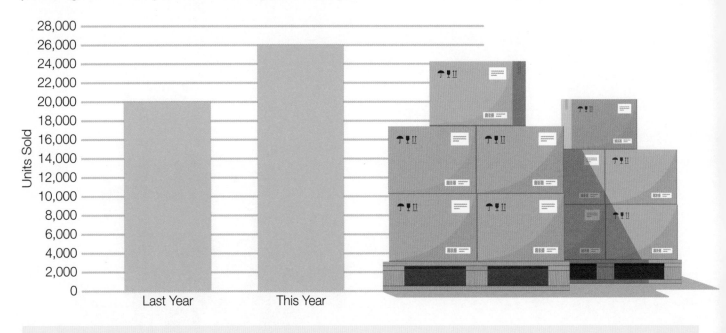

Below is a chart showing the number of units a business sold over a 6 month period. Between January and March, the selling price per unit was £15 and the variable cost per unit was £5. Due to a change in supplier, the variable cost per unit fell by 20% between April and June. Because of this, the business decided to reduce its prices by 10% during this period. Fixed costs are £60,000 per year. Based on this information, calculate the average monthly profit between January and June.

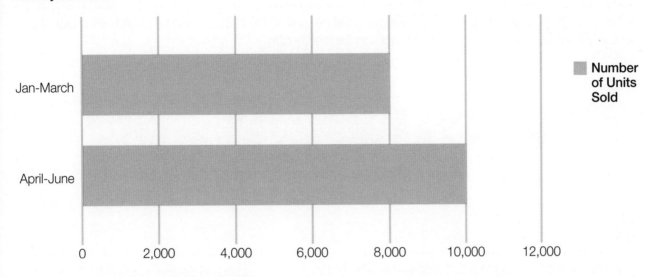

6 Break-Even

The Edexcel specification states that students only need to interpret break-even charts. However, one activity has been included that requires the construction of a break-even chart as this can deepen understanding.

Question 1

A business has an average selling price of £2.50. Variable cost per unit is 1/5 of the selling price and last month the business sold 20,000 units. Calculate the total contribution for last month.

Question 2

Opposite is a table of data relating to a fast food restaurant. The restaurant is considering increasing its average selling price by £0.20. The owner believes that this will result in demand falling by 2%. Based on this information, calculate the difference in total monthly contribution before and after the proposed price rise.

Average Selling Price	£3.00
Variable Cost Per Unit	£1.20
Monthly Units Sold	24,000

Question 3

A cupcake business pays £50 for a stand at a local market on a Saturday. The selling price per cupcake is £2.50 and the variable cost per cupcake is £1.25. Calculate the break-even point.

Question 4

Last year, a business had weekly fixed costs of £5,000. Selling price per unit was £150 and the variable cost per unit was £20. The number of units sold yearly was 6,000. Calculate the yearly margin of safety of the business.

Question 5

A business has fixed costs of £6,000 per month. The selling price per unit is £4 and the variable cost per unit is £0.80. The business is considering moving to larger premises which will result in fixed costs increasing by 4%. The business sells 5,000 units per month. Calculate the difference in the monthly margin of safety before and after the proposed move.

Question 6

An entrepreneur is assessing the viability of opening a new sandwich takeaway business and wishes to calculate the weekly break-even point. He estimates that his fixed costs will be £600 per week. The average selling price of each sandwich will be £4 and his variable cost per unit will equal 50% of the selling price. He anticipates that he will sell 200 sandwiches per day and the business will be open 6 days a week.

6.1 Using this information, complete the table below and construct a weekly break-even chart for the sandwich takeaway business.

Units	Total Revenue	Variable Costs	Fixed Costs	Total Costs
0				
200				
400				
600				
800				
1,000				
1,200				

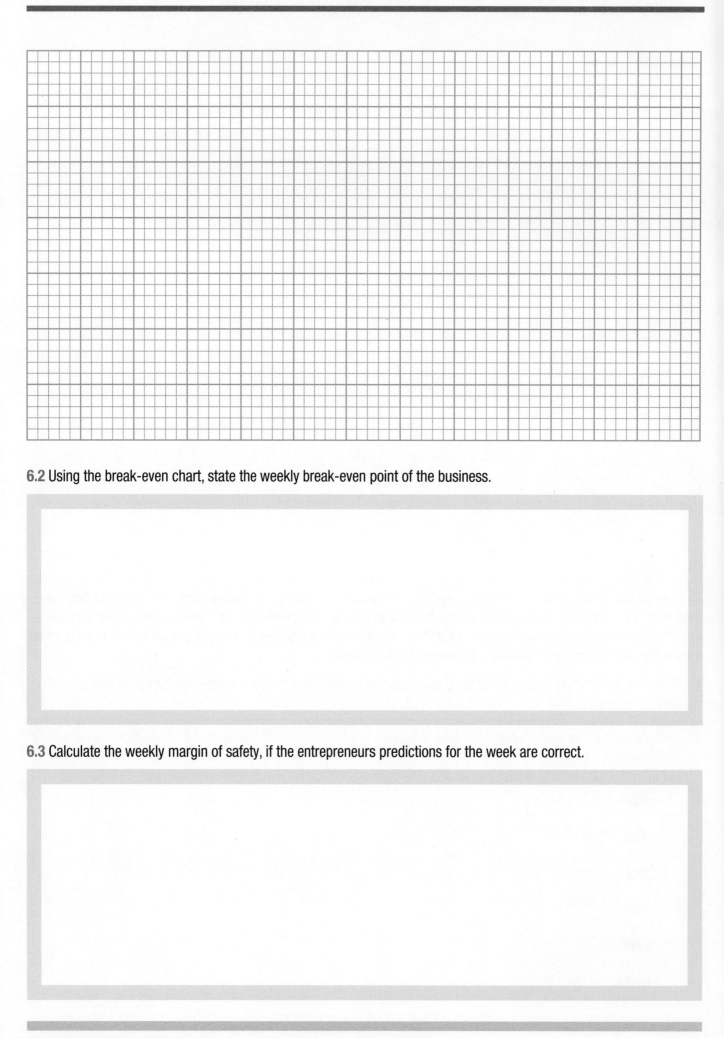

6.2 Using the break-even chart, state the weekly break-even point of the business.

6.3 Calculate the weekly margin of safety, if the entrepreneurs predictions for the week are correct.

Question 7

Below is a break-even chart for an established retailing business.

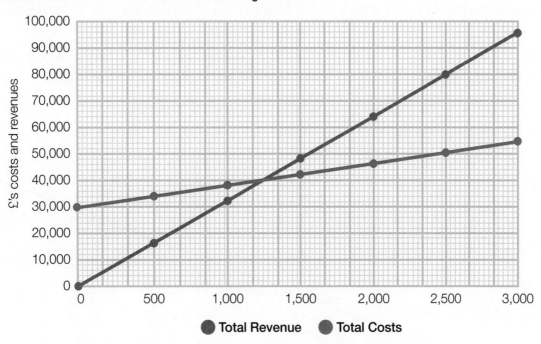

7.1 Using the break-even chart, calculate the total contribution at 2,500 units.

7.2 Using the break-even chart, calculate the variable cost per unit.

7.3 Using the break-even chart, calculate the profit or loss made at 3,000 units.

Question 8

The monthly break-even situation for a business is shown in the chart below. Due to changes in market conditions, the variable cost per unit of the business is expected to rise by 50%. As a result, the business is now planning to increase its selling price, to ensure it can still maintain the same contribution per unit on each item sold.

8.1 Amend the break-even chart below, to show both the new total revenue line and the new total cost line after the increases to these two variables. Label the new revenue line TR2 and the new total cost line TC2.

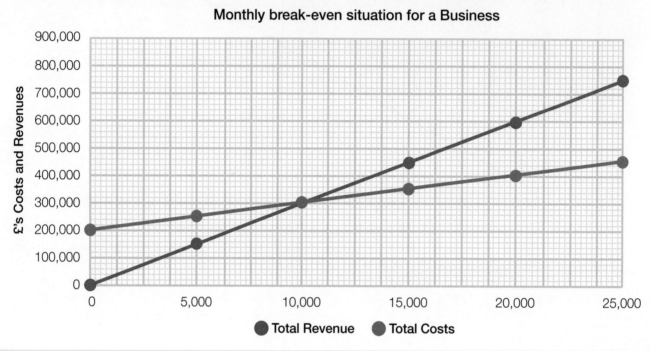

8.2 Using the break-even chart, state the difference between the new and original break-even points.

Question 9

Below is a chart which shows the number of units sold by a medium sized business over the last 5 years. In 2016, the business achieved a total contribution of £150,000. The selling price per unit is £5. Based on this information and using the chart below, calculate the variable cost per unit for 2016.

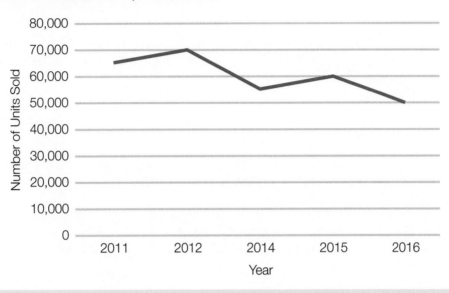

Question 10

Below is a table of data relating to a sweet manufacturer. The sweets are packaged in cardboard tubes, which account for 10p of the variable costs. The business is looking to change supplier, which will reduce the cost of the packaging by 50%. Based on this information, calculate the difference in break-even before and after the proposed change in supplier.

Yearly Fixed Costs	£18,000
Variable Costs	£0.80
Selling price (to retailer)	£1.20

7 Budgets

Question 1
....

Last year, a business had a profit budget of £450,000. This year its profit budget is 5% higher. Calculate the profit budget of the business for this year.

Question 2
....

Due to a reduction in costs, a retail business estimates that its expenditure budget this year will be 2% lower than its expenditure budget last year, which was £250,000. Calculate its expenditure budget for this year.

Question 3
....

In December, a newsagent set a revenue budget of £25,000. Its expenditure budget for December was 1/5 lower than the revenue budget. Calculate the expenditure budget for the newsagent in December.

Question 4

In January, the same newsagent had a revenue budget that was 15% higher than the revenue budget set for December. The expenditure budget was also 2/5 higher than the expenditure budget for December. Using this information and your answer to question 3, calculate the profit budget for the newsagent in January.

Question 5

Below is a revenue, expenditure and profit budget for a restaurant in July and August.

| | July | | August | |
	Budget	Actual	Budget	Actual
Revenue				
Food	5,000	5,500	5,250	5,800
Drink	1,500	1,750	1,800	1,900
Total Revenue	6,500	7,250	7,050	7,700
Expenditure				
Stock	1,000	1,100	1,150	1,250
Wages	800	900	900	1,000
Other costs	100	90	110	120
Total Expenditure	1,900	2,090	2,160	2,370
Profit/ Loss	4,600	5,160	4,890	5,330

After analysing the actual revenue and expenditure in August, the owner of the restaurant estimates that in September, revenue from both food and drink will increase by 6%. Expenditure on stock will reduce by 2% due to a change in supplier. All other costs will remain in line with the actual spend for August. Based on this information, calculate the profit/ loss budget for September.

Question 6

Last year, a manufacturer set a profit budget of £850,000. Its actual profit was £730,000. Calculate the profit variance stating whether it is adverse or favourable.

Question 7

In January, a business set a revenue budget of £325,000. Actual revenue was £50,000 lower than budget. The expenditure budget of the business in January was £210,000. Actual expenditure was 8% higher than budget. Calculate the profit variance of the business for January, stating whether it is adverse or favourable.

Question 8

Below is a chart showing the profit budget and actual profit for a designer clothes store in January and February.

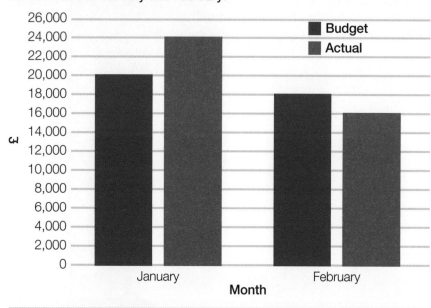

Calculate the total (combined) profit variance for January and February stating whether it is adverse or favourable.

Question 9

Below is an extract from the budget of a cycling shop in October.

| | October | |
	Budget	Actual
Revenue		
Store Revenue	£22,000	
Online Revenue	£6,000	
Total Revenue		
Expenditure		
Wages	£8,000	
Stock	£6,000	
Other costs	£2,000	
Total Expenditure		

Store revenue was actually 5% higher than budget, whereas online revenue was 4/5 of the amount that had been budgeted. Wages were £500 higher than budget, whereas stock was 2% lower than budget. Other costs (actual) were £2,100. Complete the table and calculate the profit variance for October stating whether it was adverse or favourable.

Question 10

Below shows the budgeted and actual revenue and expenditure for a business in March, April and May. Calculate the total (combined) profit variance for March, April and May, stating whether it is adverse or favourable.

	March		April		May	
	Budget £	Actual £	Budget £	Actual £	Budget £	Actual £
Total Revenue	175,000	184,000	182,000	190,000	205,000	208,000
Total Expenditure	162,000	170,000	171,000	178,000	182,000	181,000

8 Profit

Note: Profit for the year and profit for the year margin are also known as net profit and net profit margin.

Question 1

Last year, a business had sales revenue of £3.25m. The table below shows its profitability margins. Calculate last year's gross profit, operating profit and profit for the year.

	%
Gross profit margin	54
Operating profit margin	12
Profit for the year margin	4.5

Question 2

The table below shows the profit figures for a business after a year of trading. Calculate the gross profit margin, operating profit margin and profit for the year margin.

	£
Sales revenue	450,000
Gross profit	85,000
Operating profit	28,000
Profit for the year	15,400

Question 3

Last year, a retailer had the following revenue and cost data (shown in the table below). Calculate the gross profit, operating profit **and** profit for the year figures and margins of the business.

	£
Revenue	1,255,000
Cost of sales	480,000
Operating expenses	350,000
Interest	85,500

Question 4

The following year, the same retailer had the following changes to its costs and revenue figures. These are shown in the table below. Calculate the gross profit, operating profit and profit for the year figures **and** the margins for the following year of the business.

	Last Year	Following Year
	£	% change
Revenue	1,255,000	15% increase
Cost of sales	480,000	22% increase
Operating expenses	350,000	5% increase
Interest	85,500	8% increase

Question 5

A business has 3 different product lines, A, B and C. Last year, the business had operating expenses of £500,000 and interest of £72,000. Using the revenue and gross profit margins from the table below, calculate the overall operating profit margin and profit for the year margin for last year.

	Revenue	Gross Profit Margin
Product A	£140,000	45%
Product B	£360,000	38%
Product C	£780,500	52%

Question 6

A large manufacturer with sales revenue of £10.6m had the following profit margins for last year. Using the data from the chart, calculate the gross profit, operating profit and profit for the year.

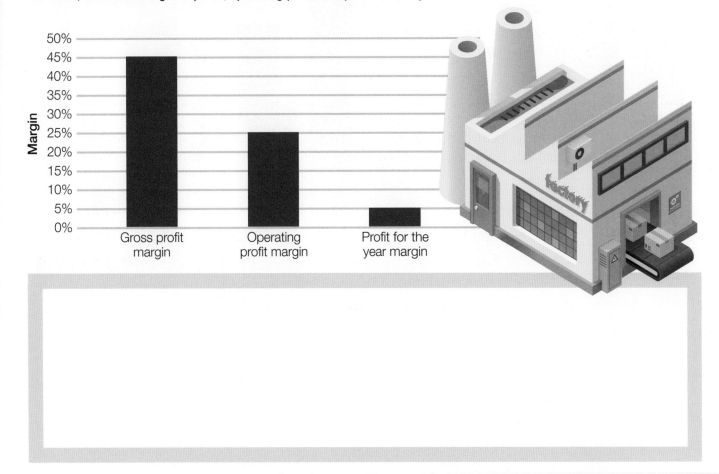

Question 7

The following year, the same manufacturer had an increase in sales revenue of 11%. Its gross profit figure increased by 5%, its operating profit increased by 4%, but its profit for the year figure decreased by 2%, due to a significant increase in finance costs. Using the data from question 6, calculate the gross, operating profit and profit for the year margins for the following year.

Question 8

A business with four product lines, 1, 2, 3 and 4, has operating expenses of £450,000 and revenue of £2.8m. The amount of revenue generated by each product is detailed in the pie chart below and its respective gross profit margins are detailed in the bar chart. Using the data in both charts, calculate the overall gross profit margin for the firm and the operating profit margin.

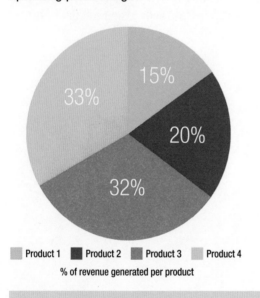

% of revenue generated per product

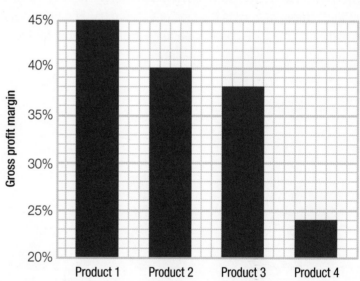

Question 9

The sales revenue of a business for the last two years is shown on the chart below. Last year, the operating profit margin of the business was 12% and two years ago the operating profit margin was 8%. Calculate the profit for the year margin for both years, assuming interest accounted for 5% of operating profit.

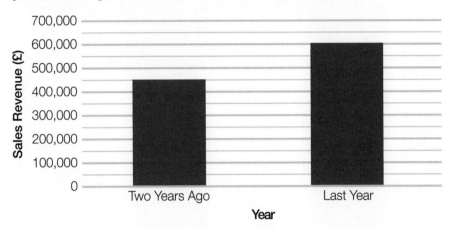

Question 10

This year, the business in question 9 is estimating a 15% increase in revenue and operating profit of £52,400. Assuming 5% of operating profit for interest, calculate the operating profit margin and profit for the year margin for this year.

9 Liquidity

Question 1

A business has current assets of £200,000 and current liabilities of £160,000. Calculate the current ratio of the business.

Question 2

The table below shows an extract from the company accounts of a business.

Inventory	£300,000
Receivables	£100,000
Cash	£200,000
Payables	£160,000
Bank overdraft	£240,000

Calculate the current ratio and the acid test ratio of the business.

Question 3

A business has a current ratio of 1.8:1. Its current liabilities are £2 million. Calculate the current assets of the business.

Question 4

A business has £500,000 of inventory, £100,000 of receivables and £200,000 cash. The current liabilities of the business are 20% lower than the current assets. Calculate the current ratio and acid test ratio of the business.

Question 5

The table below shows an extract from the company accounts of a business.

Inventory	£200,000
Receivables	£50,000
Cash	£100,000
Payables	£150,000
Bank overdraft	£50,000

The business has decided to purchase £20,000 of inventory using cash as well as clearing the bank overdraft, also using cash. Calculate the current ratio and acid test ratio of the business before and after the purchase of the inventory and the clearing of the overdraft.

10 Capacity Utilisation

Question 1

A business currently has the capacity to produce 50,000 units per week. The business is looking at increasing its capacity by 8%. Calculate the new capacity based on the 8% increase.

Question 2

This year, a factory has the capacity to produce 441,000 units. Last year, the business's capacity was 5% lower. Calculate the total capacity of the firm last year.

Question 3

A business is currently producing 17,000 units per week. It has the capacity to produce 25,000 units per week. Calculate the capacity utilisation of the business.

Question 4

Last Saturday night, 476 people watched a play at a theatre. The capacity utilisation was 85%. Calculate the total capacity of the theatre.

Question 5

A daily newspaper has the capacity to publish 10 million newspapers a year. Last year, daily sales of the newspaper were 24,000 and all papers produced were sold. The newspaper is available 5 days per week, 50 weeks of the year. Calculate the newpaper's capacity utilisation for last year.

Question 6

Below is a chart that shows how many units a business produced between January and June. The business has the capacity to produce 100,000 units per month. Calculate the average capacity utilisation between January and June.

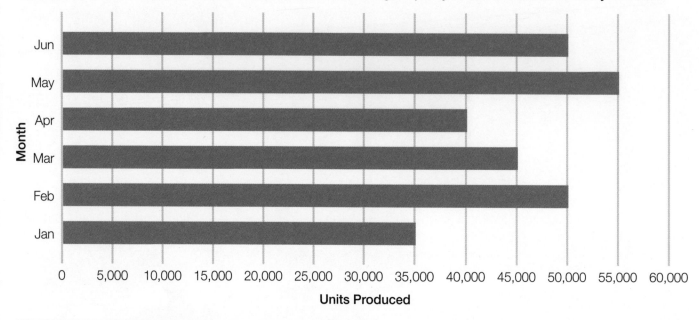

Question 7

Last season, a football club had an average attendance of 42,750 people per match, a capacity utilisation of 95%. The club is considering extending the ground which will increase total capacity by 20%. Calculate the total increase in capacity after the proposed expansion.

Question 8

A local cinema has 3 screens of equal size. The average capacity utilisation is 60% across the three screens which equates to 450 customers. To increase capacity utilisation, the cinema is considering reducing the number of screens from three to two. Calculate the new capacity utlisation of the cinema, based on on the planned reduction of screens and assuming the number of customers remains the same.

Question 9

A lawnmower manufacturer has a capacity utilisation of 75%. It is looking at increasing its capacity by 10%. Calculate the new capacity utilisation assuming the manufacturer produces the same number of lawnmowers.

Question 10

A manufacturer is currently operating at 95% capacity utilisation, producing 237,500 units per year. The manufacturer has just secured a new contract to produce a further 100,000 units next year, and is therefore moving to a new factory with a bigger capacity. The new factory has the capacity to produce 7/8 more units than the current factory. Calculate the capacity utilisation for the business next year.

11 Stock Control

Below is a stock control chart for one component that a small manufacturing company uses in its manufacturing process.

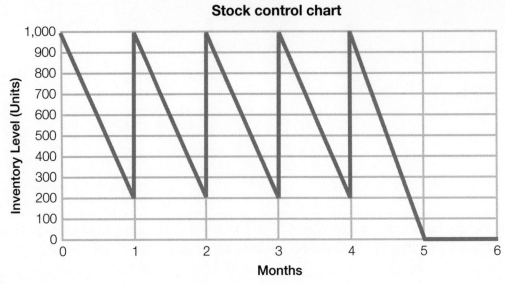

Stock control chart

Question 1

Calculate the average daily usage of this component during months 1-5 inclusive, assuming there are 30 days in each month.

Question 2

What is the normal level of buffer inventory held by the business?

Question 3

For month 1 only, calculate the re-order level of the component, if an order is triggered after 40% of the total firm's inventory holding has been used in that month.

Question 4

Calculate the normal lead time for delivery of the component.

Question 5

Due to a supplier problem during month 5, the manufacturer needs to increase production in month 6 and therefore requires an additional 75% extra volume of this component to be delivered in addition to the usual delivery. Calculate the required re-order quantity of the component the business needs to receive in month 6, to meet the increased level of demand and return the business to hold the normal level of buffer inventory.

12 Quantitative Sales Forecasting

Question 1

Below is a table of data showing the yearly sales revenue of a business.
Using the data in the table, calculate a three-year moving average.

Year	Sales (£000)	Three-year moving total (£000)	Three-year moving average (£000)
2009	700		
2010	1,100		
2011	1,000		
2012	1,200		
2013	1,400		
2014	1,300		
2015	1,800		
2016	2,000		

Question 2

Calculate the cyclical variation for 2011 and 2015.

Question 3

Below is a table of data showing the yearly sales revenue of a business. Using the data in the table, calculate a three-year moving average, the cyclical variation for each year and the average cyclical variation.

Year	Sales (£000)	Three-year moving total (£000)	Three-year moving average (£000)	Variation (£000)
2007	225			
2008	240			
2009	240			
2010	360			
2011	240			
2012	340			
2013	330			
2014	380			
2015	280			
2016	420			

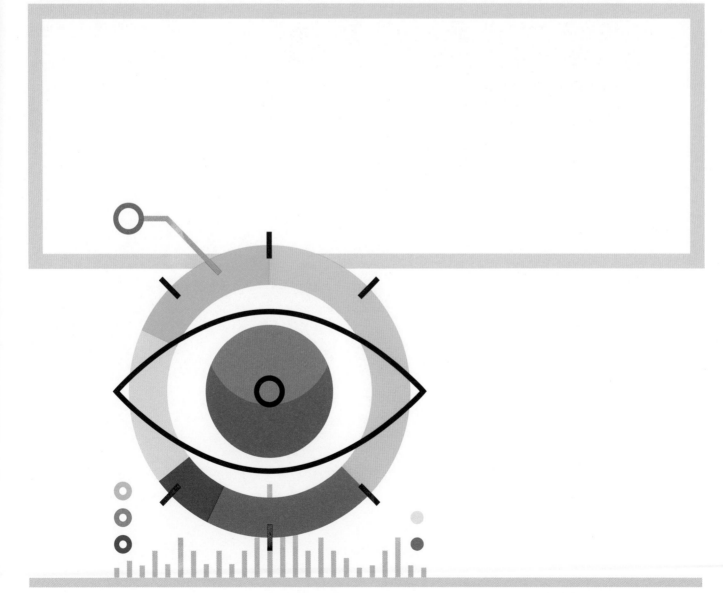

Question 4

Below is a table of data showing the quarterly sales of a business. Using the data in the table, calculate a four-quarter moving average.

Year	Quarter	Sales (units)	Four-quarter moving total (units)	Eight-quarter moving total (units)	Four-quarter moving average (units)
2013	3	8,000			
	4	9,000			
2014	1	11,000			
	2	12,000			
	3	9,000			
	4	10,000			
2015	1	13,000			
	2	15,000			
	3	11,000			
	4	12,000			
2016	1	16,000			
	2	18,000			

13 Investment Appraisal

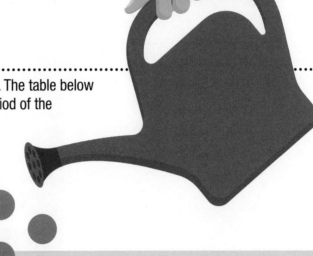

Payback

Question 1

A business is considering an investment at a cost of £200,000. The table below shows the projected net cash flows. Calculate the payback period of the proposed investment.

Year 1	£50,000
Year 2	£60,000
Year 3	£60,000
Year 4	£80,000

Question 2

The payback on an investment is estimated to be 3 years and 8 months. Net cash flows in Year 1 are estimated to be £60,000, £70,000 in Year 2 and £90,000 in Year 3. The estimated cost of the investment is £300,000. Calculate the estimated net cash flows in Year 4.

A business is looking at investing £325,000 in a new website with an e-commerce facility. The table below shows the projected cash inflows and cash outflows. Calculate the payback period of the new website.

Year	Inflows	Outflows
0		£325,000
1	£150,000	£50,000
2	£180,000	£60,000
3	£200,000	£80,000
4	£250,000	£110,000

Question 4

After some consideration, the above business believes that in Year 3, the cash inflows and outflows will be 10% higher than estimated. Calculate the new payback period based on this information.

A manufacturing business is looking to invest in further automation at a cost of £1.7m. Below is a chart showing the projected inflows and outflows. Calculate the payback period of the proposed investment.

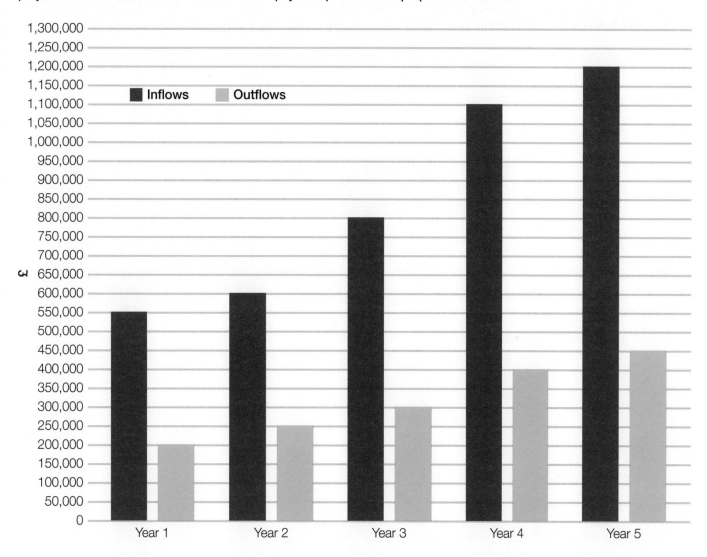

Average (Accounting) Rate of Return (ARR)

A small coffee shop is looking to open a second shop. The total cost of the investment will be £120,000. The shop owner believes that net cash flows will be £37,000 each year, for a period of 4 years. Calculate the ARR for the new shop.

A business is considering an investment of £140,000. The business estimates that total cash inflows over a 5 year period will be £600,000 and total cash outflows will be £400,000 over a 5 year period. Calculate the ARR of the proposed investment.

A large chain of DIY stores is looking to expand into a new town. The business has been presented with two possible sites for a new store, site A and site B.

Site A has an initial investment cost of £1,400,000 and estimated cash outflows of £100,000 per year for 5 years. The DIY chain estimates that cash inflows will be £425,000 each year for 5 years.

Site B has an initial investment cost of £2,000,000 and cash outflows of £40,000 per year for 5 years. The DIY chain estimates that cash inflows will be ¼ higher than the yearly estimated cash inflows of Site A.

Calculate the ARR for each potential new site.

To take advantage of a gap in the market, an entrepreneur is looking to open a tanning salon on the local high street. The entrepreneur believes that the intial cost of establishing the business will be £100,000. The table below shows the estimated cash inflows and outflows over the next 5 years. Using the information above and from the table, calculate the ARR of opening the tanning salon.

Year	Inflows	Outflows
0		£100,000
1	£120,000	£220,000
2	£150,000	£170,000
3	£180,000	£130,000
4	£240,000	£130,000
5	£260,000	£120,000

Question 5

An ice cream seller has two options to expand his business for the summer season, June – September inclusive.

Option 1 is to rent an ice cream van for an initial investment of £4,000, which the seller believes will result in net cash flows of £1,500 in June, increasing by 20% per month each month until September.

Option 2 is to rent a beach shack, which will increase the summer season to October. The cost of renting a beach shack is an initial investment of £6,000 and the seller believes this will lead to net cash flows of £2,500 per month, except in October when net cash flows are expected to fall by 1/5.

Calculate the monthly ARR of each option for the ice cream seller.

Net Present Value

A hotel is looking at increasing the number of bedrooms and extending the restaurant. The cost of the investment will be £150,000. The owners of the hotel have decided to use a 7% discount rate to assess the proposed investment. Below is a table showing forecasted net cash flows over the next 3 years. Calculate the net present value of the proposed investment.

Year	Net Cash Flows
0	(£150,000)
1	£175,000
2	£220,000
3	£280,000

Year	0	1	2	3
7% Discount Factor	1	0.935	0.873	0.816

Question 2

A manufacturing business is considering investing £120,000 in a new automation system that will help improve productivity. The table below shows the forecasted cash inflows and outflows from the proposed investment. It has decided to assess the investment using a discount rate of 5%. Calculate the net present value of the proposed investment.

Year	Inflows	Outflows
0	0	£120,000
1	£50,000	£20,000
2	£60,000	£20,000
3	£70,000	£30,000
4	£90,000	£35,000
5	£100,000	£20,000

Year	0	1	2	3	4	5
5% Discount Factor	1	0.952	0.907	0.864	0.823	0.784

Question 3

A small bakery business has identified two possible pieces of machinery that can help it increase productivity. The owners have decided to use a 5% discount rate to assess the proposed investment. Based purely on net present value, which machine should the owners choose.

Machine 1: £200,000

Forecasted yearly net cash flows

Year 1: £40,000
Year 2: £55,000
Year 3: £70,000
Year 4: £83,000
Year 5: £91,000

Machine 2: £300,000

Forecasted yearly net cash flows

Year 1: £90,000
Year 2: £94,000
Year 3: £106,000
Year 4: £120,000
Year 5: £125,000

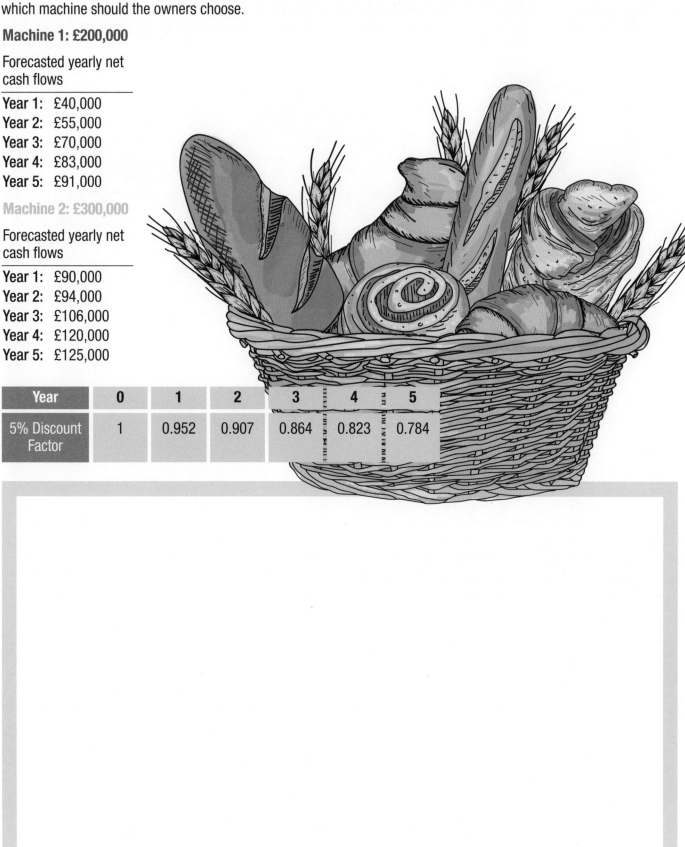

Year	0	1	2	3	4	5
5% Discount Factor	1	0.952	0.907	0.864	0.823	0.784

A factory is looking at increasing production space at a cost of £450,000. Over 5 years, the owners believe that it would generate total cash inflows of £1,300,000. The pie chart below shows the percentage of total cash inflows that will be generated in each of the 5 years. The estimated outflows are 5% of yearly cash inflows. The owners have decided to use a discount rate of 10% to assess the investment. Calculate the net present value of the proposed investment.

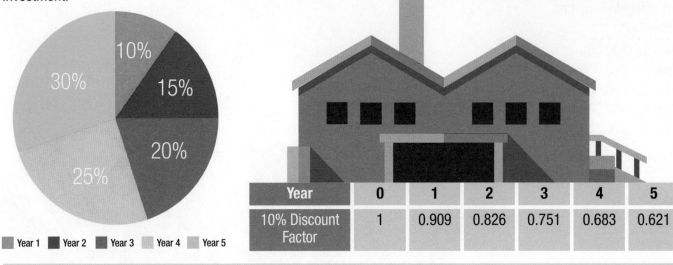

| Year 1 | Year 2 | Year 3 | Year 4 | Year 5 |

Year	0	1	2	3	4	5
10% Discount Factor	1	0.909	0.826	0.751	0.683	0.621

A business is looking to invest £100,000 in new e-commerce software. Year 1 cash inflows are estimated to be £60,000 and are forecast to increase by 10% per year, for the following two years. The outflows are estimated to be 1/5 of yearly cash inflows. The owners of the business have decided to use a 10% discount rate when assessing the investment. Calculate the net present value of the proposed investment.

Year	0	1	2	3
10% Discount Factor	1	0.909	0.826	0.751

14 Decision Trees

Question 1

A business is considering developing a new product. The probability of the new product being a success is 0.7 and should lead to an extra £500,000 in sales. The probability of failure is 0.3 and this would lead to additional sales of £50,000. Calculate the expected value of the new product.

Question 2

The business in question 1 has re-evaluated the new product option and now believes that the probability of the new product being a success will be 0.6 and the probability of the new product being a failure will be 0.4. The business also believes that if the product is a success then sales revenue will be 5% higher than originally estimated, but if it fails the additional sales generated will be as previously predicted. Calculate the new expected value.

Question 3

A clothes shop is considering opening a second retail outlet. The cost of opening this second outlet is estimated to be £80,000. The probability of the new retail outlet being a success is 0.8 and would result in £220,000 of revenue being generated. The probability of failure is 0.2 which would result in £90,000 of revenue being gained. Calculate the net gain of the proposal.

Question 4

A pub is considering converting its first floor into 10 rooms which can be let out on a bed and breakfast basis. The table below contains the forecasted data of the proposed conversion. Construct a decision tree and calculate the expected value and net gain of the proposed conversion.

Cost of investment	£180,000
Probability of revenue being £340,000 (high sales) per year	0.6
Probability of revenue being £210,000 (low sales) per year	0.4

Question 5

A travel agent is considering either investing further in its e-commerce system or opening a new branch in a different part of town. The table below contains the forecasted data for both options. Calculate the expected value and net gain of both options and state which option should be chosen based on the data.

E-Commerce System	
Cost of Investment	£80,000
Probability of revenue being £120,000	0.7
Probability of revenue being £40,000	0.3

New Branch	
Cost of Investment	£65,000
Probability of revenue being £90,000	0.8
Probability of revenue being £55,000	0.2

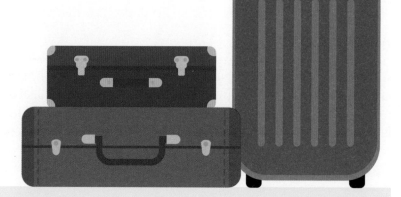

Question 6

A business is looking at two options to increase sales.

Option 1

Probability of high sales is 0.6 which would result in sales being £50,000. Probability of low sales is 0.4 and would result in sales being 1/8 lower than if sales were high. The cost of this option is £20,000.

Option 2

Probability of high sales is 0.7 and would result in sales being 15% higher than if sales were low. Probability of sales being low is 0.3 and would result in sales being £40,000. The cost of this option is £18,000.

Calculate the expected value and net gain of both options and state which option should be chosen based on the data.

Question 7

A local supermarket is considering two options to increase sales. One option is to reduce prices; the other option is to increase promotion. Opposite is a decision tree outlining the cost, probability and expected sales from both options.

Calculate the expected value and net gain of both options and state which option should be chosen based on the data.

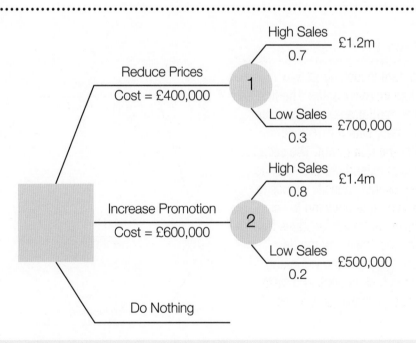

Question 8

A UK holiday park company is considering two options to increase profits. One option is to open a further park in the UK. The other option is to open a park in the south of France.

UK Park

The cost of opening a further park in the UK is estimated to be £1.5 million. The probability of the venture being a success is 0.7. This would result in estimated sales of £2.2 million. Failure would result in estimated sales of £800,000.

South of France Park

The cost of opening a park in the south of France is estimated to be £2.2 million. The probability of the venture being a success is 0.6. This would result in estimated sales of £3 million. Failure would result in estimated sales of £1.8 million.

Calculate the expected value and net gain of both options and state which option the business should choose based on the data.

Question 9

A restaurant is looking at two options to increase sales. The first option is to offer a delivery service to customers within a 10 mile radius of the restaurant. The second option is to extend the premises to increase overall capacity. Opposite is a decision tree outlining the cost, probability and expected sales from both options. Based on the data, calculate the expected value and net gain of both options and state which option should be chosen.

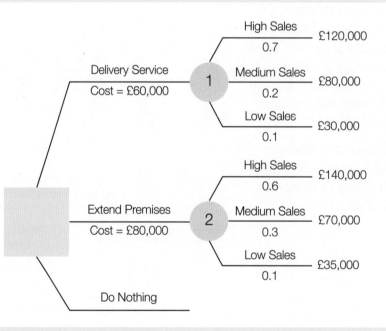

A car showroom is considering 2 different options to increase sales. The first option is to increase the size of the sales team by employing 5 new staff. This will cost £200,000. The probability that this will result in high sales is 0.7 and should result in sales of £500,000. The probability of low sales is 0.3 and if sales are low, then this will result in sales of £250,000.

The second option is to extend the size of the showroom to accommodate more vehicles. The cost of the extension is estimated to be £80,000. The probability of high sales is 0.6, the probability of medium sales is 0.3 and the probability of low sales is 0.1. Low sales have been estimated to be £180,000, medium sales have been estimated to be £240,000 and high sales have been estimated to be £350,000.

Construct a decision tree and calculate the expected value and net gain of both options. State which option the business should choose based on the data.

15 Critical Path Analysis

The Edexcel specification does not require students to be able to construct network diagrams, however, two activities have been included that require network diagrams to be constructed, as this can help deepen understanding.

(All the activities are in weeks)

Question 1

The network diagram below shows the activities involved in extending the premises of a café to increase capacity. Calculate the earliest start time for node 6 and the latest finish time for node 5.

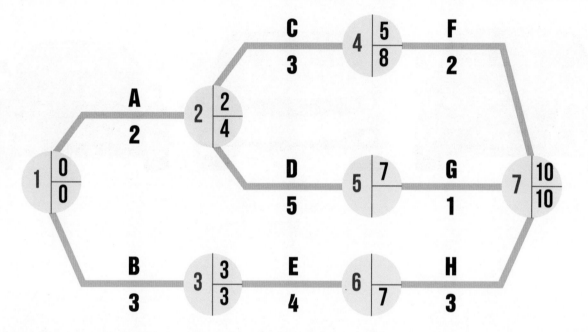

Question 2

The network diagram below shows the activities involved in a retailer opening a new store. Calculate the earliest start times for nodes 3 and 6 and the latest finish times for nodes 2 and 5.

The network diagram below shows the activities involved in launching a new product. Calculate the earliest start times for nodes 5, 7 and 8 and the latest finish times for nodes 2, 3 and 4.

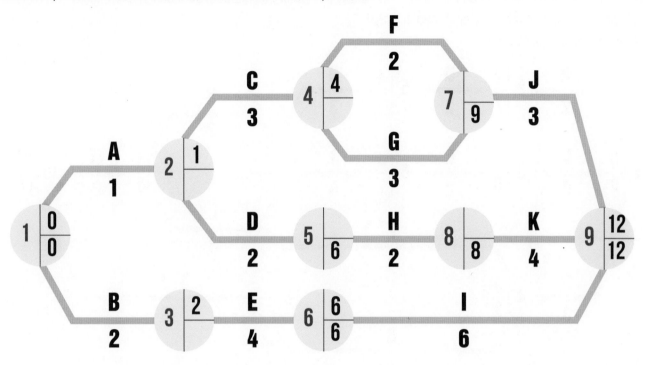

Question 4

The network diagram below shows the activities involved in a manufacturer off-shoring production overseas.

A Calculate the earliest start times for nodes 7 and 8 and the latest finish times for nodes 5, 6, 7 and 8

B Calculate the total float for activity D and activity I

C Write down the critical path

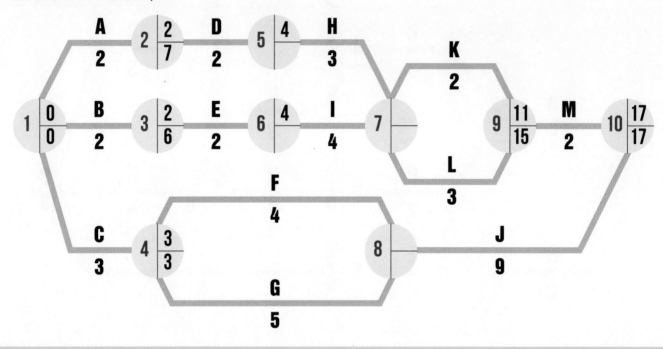

Question 5

The manufacturer in question 4 now believes that activity H will take 9 weeks instead of 3 weeks. Based on this information, calculate the earliest start time for node 7 and the new completion time.

The network diagram below shows the activities involved in a new promotional campaign for a business.

A Calculate the earliest start times and latest finish times for each node

B Calculate the total float for activity G

C Write down the critical path

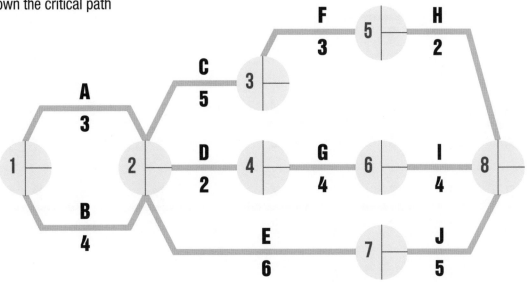

The network diagram below shows the activities involved in a large building project. Calculate the earliest start time and latest finish times for all the nodes and write down the critical path.

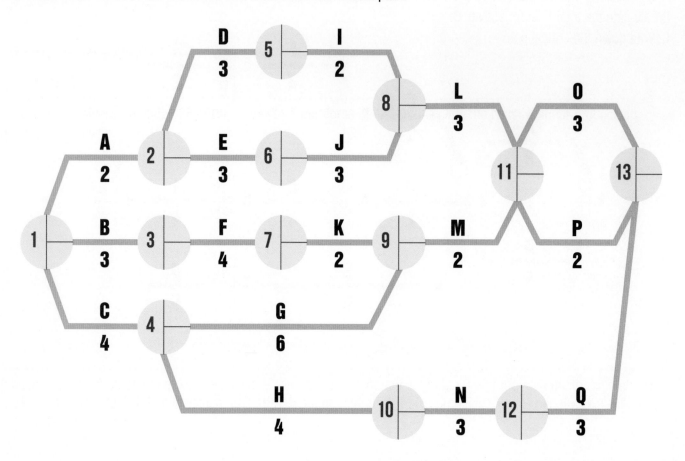

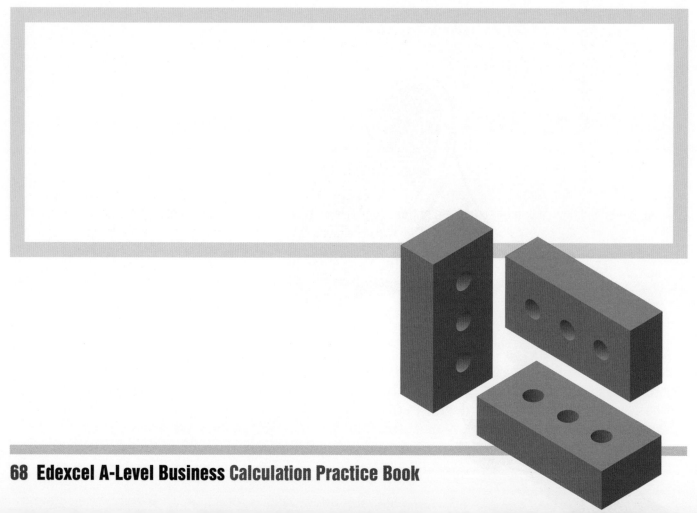

A senior construction manager has reviewed the estimated times for the building project in question 7 and believes some of the durations are incorrect. Activity A is estimated to take 3 weeks longer, activity E is estimated to take 2 weeks longer and activity L is estimated to take 1 week longer. Change the durations for activities A, E and L and re-calculate the earliest start times and latest finish times for all the nodes. Write down the new critical path.

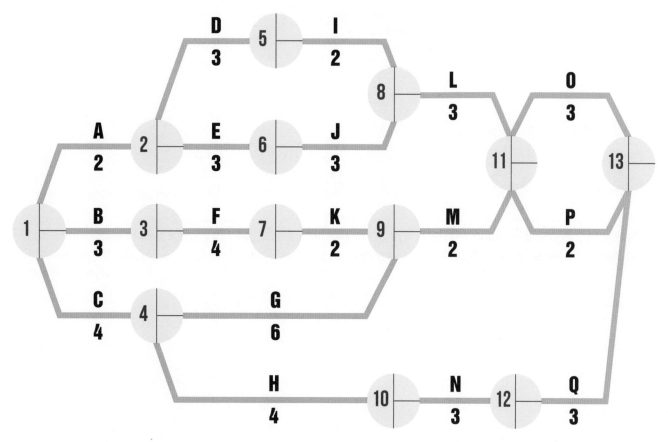

The table below shows the activities, preceding activities and durations for a project.

A Construct a network diagram for the project

B Calculate the earliest start times and latest finish times for all nodes

C Write down the critical path

Activity	Preceding activities	Duration (weeks)
A	-	2
B	-	4
C	A	3
D	A	2
E	B	4
F	C, D	2
G	F, E	2
H	F, E	3
I	G, H	1

The table below shows the activities, preceding activities and durations for a project.

A Construct a network diagram for the project

B Calculate the earliest start times and latest finish times for all nodes

C Write down the critical path

Activity	Preceding activities	Duration (weeks)
A	-	2
B	-	2
C	-	3
D	A	3
E	A	4
F	B	1
G	C	3
H	D, E	2
I	F	6
J	G	4
K	H, I, J	2

16 Ratio Analysis

Gearing

Question 1

A business has non-current liabilities of £300,000 and total equity of £500,000. Calculate the gearing ratio of the business.

Question 2

The table opposite shows an extract from the company accounts of a business. Calculate the gearing ratio of the business.

Current assets	£5 million
Current liabilities	£2 million
Non-current liabilities	£9 million
Capital employed	£15 million

Question 3

Last year, a business had a gearing ratio of 20%. The capital employed of the business was £5m. Calculate the value of non-current liabilities for the business last year.

Question 4

The table below is an extract from the company accounts of a manufacturer.

Non-current liabilities	£6.75m
Total equity	£8.25 million

The manufacturer is considering increasing capacity at a cost of £2 million. This would be funded via long-term borrowing. Calculate the current gearing ratio and the new gearing ratio of the business based on the additional long-term borrowing.

Question 5

The table below is an extract from the company accounts of a business.

Current assets	£10 million
Current liabilities	£4 million
Capital employed	£19 million

The non-current liabilities of the business are 90% higher than its current liabilities. The business is considering an investment of £8 million, all of which would need to be funded via long-term borrowing. Calculate the current gearing ratio of the business and the new gearing ratio of the business based on the additional long-term borrowing.

Return on Capital Employed

Question 1

A business has operating profit of £4 million and capital employed of £20 million. Calculate the return on capital employed of the business.

Question 2

Last year, a business had a return on capital employed of 15%. Capital employed last year was £12 million. Calculate the operating profit of the business for last year.

Question 3

The table below shows an extract from the company accounts of a business.

Non-current liabilities	£14 million
Total equity	£7 million
Operating profit	£2 million

Calculate the return on capital employed of the business.

Question 4

Last year, a business had an operating profit margin of 8%. Revenue was £2.5 million, total equity was £1 million and non-current liabilities were £250,000. Calculate the return on capital employed for the business last year.

Question 5

The table below shows an extract from the company accounts of a business.

Revenue	£5 million
Cost of sales	£2 million
Operating expenses	£1.9 million
Non-current liabilities	£0.5 million
Total equity	£1.8 million

Calculate the return on capital employed of the business.

17 Human Resources

Labour Productivity

Question 1

Last year, a business produced 364,000 units with a workforce of 4,000. Calculate the weekly labour productivity per worker last year.

Question 2

A business has 84 members of staff of which 5/7 are involved in manufacturing. 50% of the manufacturing staff will work on any individual shift. It is estimated that each member of staff should produce 15 units per shift. Calculate the total production per shift.

Question 3

The following year, the firm in question 2 increases its total manufacturing staff by 6 members, which leads to total output rising by 10% per shift. Calculate the labour productivity per shift.